James'
Busy Day

Illustrated by Peter Lawson
Series Editor: Teresa Wilson

Thomas the Tank Engine & Friends

A BRITT ALLCROFT COMPANY PRODUCTION

Based on The Railway Series by The Rev W Awdry

© Gullane (Thomas) LLC 2003

Published in Great Britain in 2003 by Egmont Books Limited,
239 Kensington High Street, London, W8 6SA
Printed in China
ISBN 0 7498 5754 4

10 9 8 7 6 5 4 3 2 1

Educational consultant: Nicola Morgan, literacy expert and author of over 60 early learning books.

It was James' day off.

The Fat Controller came to see him.

"I have a problem, James," he said.

"We have lots of passengers today. I need you to pull two carriages for me."

"But it's my day off," grumbled James.

"I shouldn't have to work on my day off."

"Just two carriages, James, and then you can rest," said The Fat Controller.

James grumbled as the carriages were being attached.

Just then, The Fat Controller appeared.

"James," he said, "I have another problem."

"There are now more passengers. I need you to pull three more carriages."

"But two carriages plus three more
makes five carriages altogether,"
grumbled James.

"And it IS my day off," he added.

"Just pull these five carriages.
Then you can rest," said The Fat Controller.

9

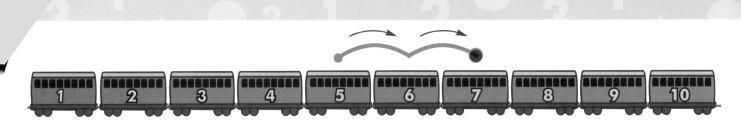

James grumbled as the carriages were being attached.

When he saw The Fat Controller coming, he knew what to expect.

"I need you to pull two more carriages for me," said The Fat Controller.

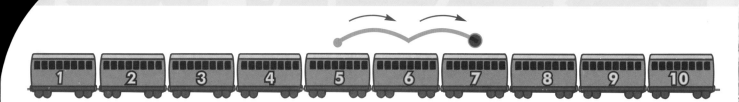

"But five carriages plus two more makes seven carriages altogether," grumbled James.

"And it IS my day off," he added.

"Just pull these seven carriages. Then you can rest," said The Fat Controller.

James set off.

He was pulling seven carriages.

They were heavy and he was tired.

At the station, lots of people got off.

The guard took two carriages off.

Now James only had five carriages to pull.

He felt a bit better.

15

James was pulling five carriages.

At the next station, two of the carriages needed to go a different way.

The guard took them off and gave them to Percy.

Now James only had three carriages to pull.

He felt a lot better.

James was pulling three carriages.

At the next station, one carriage
had a broken wheel.

The guard took the carriage off.

Now James only had two carriages to pull.

He felt much better.

It was time to go home.

Back at the station, the guard took off
the last two carriages.

Now James had no carriages to pull.

He felt very happy indeed.

Then he saw The Fat Controller coming.

21

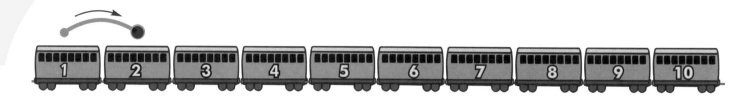

"I would like to thank you, James,
for working so hard today," he said.

"You are a Really Splendid Engine!
So I would like to give you a day off
plus one MORE day off."

"But that makes two days off altogether,"
said James.

"You really are a Splendid Fat Controller too!" he laughed.